Oxford Discover
Writing and Spelling
1

Tamzin Thompson

OXFORD
UNIVERSITY PRESS

Scope and Sequence

Writing

UNIT	WORDS TO KNOW	WRITING FOCUS	WRITING OUTPUT	PLANNING TOOLS
1 What makes a good friend? Page 4	paint share paintbrush climb tree together read help homework fun	Initial capital letters for names *Emma*	Personalized writing	Word web
2 What's your favorite picture? Page 8	poster sky moon stars clouds ocean dolphins colourful turtle beautiful	Initial capital letters and periods in a sentence *There are lots of colourful fish.*	Picture description	Word web
3 Who lives in this house? Page 12	badger woods neat messy hard-working smart shy parties cheerful kind	Using adjectives *Bertie is very neat.*	Description of a fictional character	T-chart
4 How do animals change? Page 16	life cycle lay eggs hatch tadpole tail week grow breathe adult land	Writing captions *In spring, frogs lay eggs in the water.*	Procedural text	Flowchart
5 How many days to go? Page 20	excited look forward to vacation sunhat bucket shovel camera sunglasses pack suitcase	Parts of a story: beginning, middle, and ending	Fictional story	Timeline
6 Who can you call? Page 24	emergency police fire department ambulance service dial operator panic remember accident crime	Using imperatives for instructions *Dial 911.*	Instructional poster	Flowchart
7 Where do you want to live? Page 28	the country traditional garden cozy peaceful modern busy city interesting comfortable	Labelling pictures	Descriptive text	Chart
8 What sounds can you make? Page 32	percussion instrument stomp tap pat clap click whistle hum voice	Main idea and details	Informational text	T-chart
9 What do your toys do? Page 36	robot alive train set fly plane drive dance puppet floor surprised	Parts of a story: beginning, middle, and ending	Imaginative story	Notes

Spelling Master Class

UNIT	SPELLING FOCUS / STRATEGY
1 Page 40	Keep a spelling log
2 Page 41	a_e ay ai *cake birthday paint*
3 Page 42	Plurals: *-s -es -ies* *rabbits buses brushes sandwiches boxes families*
4 Page 43	e ea ee ey y *me pea see key baby*
5 Page 44	i_e igh ie y *kite night pie fly*
6 Page 45	Verb endings: *-s -es* *walks passes watches pushes fixes goes*
7 Page 46	ow o_e oa *snow phone coat*
8 Page 47	Double consonants *running swimming getting clapping*
9 Page 48	u_e ue ew ui oo *tube glue new fruit zoo*

1 What makes a good friend?

Words to know

paint share paintbrush climb tree
together read help homework fun

Read

A Look at the photos. Who do you think the children are?

1 ☐ brothers and sisters 2 ☐ friends 3 ☐ cousins

B Read.

I'm Emma. These are my friends.

This is Ben. He paints good pictures. We share our paint and paintbrushes.

This is Carla. She climbs trees. We play together in the park.

This is Lucas. He's my brother and my friend! Lucas reads a lot. He helps me with my homework.

I have fun with my friends every day.

Understand

C What are the names of Emma's friends?

______ ______ ______

D Look at the diagrams. Write the names of the friends.

1 climbs trees / plays with Emma → ______

2 reads a lot / helps Emma → ______

3 paints / shares with Emma → ______

E Look at the diagrams in **D**. Write in the chart.

Friend	What does he / she do?	How is he / she a good friend?
Lucas		
Carla		
Ben		

F Think about Emma's friends. How are they different?
Are your friends different or the same?

Think

G **Think about your friends. Write a list of your good friends.**

H **Writing focus**

The first letter of a name is a capital letter. **E**mma

Look at your list in G. Do the names start with capital letters?

Plan

I **Choose two of your friends from G. Complete the diagram.**

1. What are their names? Write in the red shapes.
2. What do they do? Write in the blue shapes.
3. How are they good friends to you? Write in the green shapes.

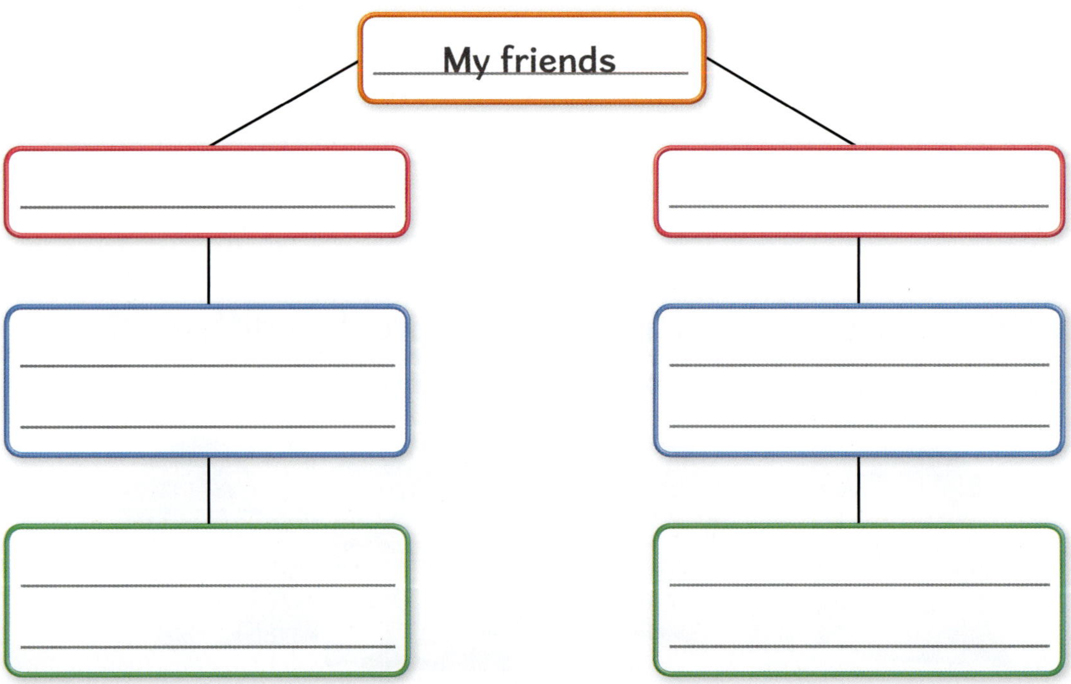

Write

J Now write about your friends. Use your work in **G**, **H** and **I** to help you. Draw or glue pictures.

I'm ______________________. These are my friends.

This is ______________________.

____

____

____

____

This is ______________________.

____

____

____

____

Edit

K Read and check.

In my writing:

☐ I can follow my writing plan.

☐ I can use a capital letter for the first letter of a name.

2 What's your favorite picture?

Words to know

poster sky moon stars clouds ocean
dolphins colorful turtle beautiful

Read

A Look at the title. What do you think the text is about?

B Read.

My favorite posters

I'm Soo Yun. These are my favorite posters.

This is a picture of the sky. The moon and stars are yellow, orange, and white. There are some white clouds, too. It's a great poster.

This is a picture of the ocean. There are two grey dolphins and many colorful fish. You can see two turtles, too. It's a beautiful poster.

Understand

C **What can you see in the posters? Read and circle.**

moon	stars	cat	fish	dolphins
ocean	cars	plants	sky	turtles
sun	books	kites	clouds	birds

D **Write the words in the correct boxes.**

Poster A	Poster B
stars	

E **Look at the table in D and the posters in B.**
Complete the sentences.

1 You can see a yellow ________________ in Poster A.
2 There are yellow, orange, and white ________________ in Poster A.
3 You can see white ________________ in Poster A.
4 You can see the blue ________________ in Poster B.
5 There are many colorful ________________ in Poster B.
6 You can see two grey ________________ in Poster B.

F **Think about Soo Yun's posters. Which is your favorite? What pictures do you have in your bedroom?**

Think

G Think about your pictures. What words describe your favorite pictures? Read and circle.

pretty | great | amazing | lovely | colorful | scary | cool | funny

Plan

H Choose one of your favorite pictures. What can you see in it? Complete the word web.

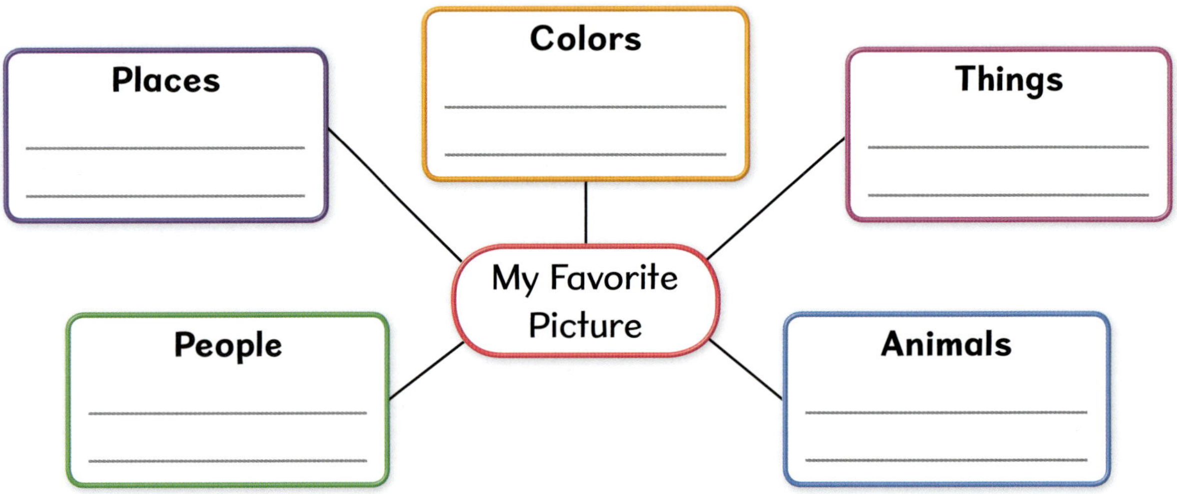

I **Writing focus**

The first letter of the first word in a sentence is a capital letter. We end a sentence with a period.

There are lots of colorful fish.

Write these sentences correctly.

1 it's a great poster

____

2 this is a picture of the ocean

____

Write

J Now write about your favorite picture. Use your work in **G**, **H**, and **I** to help you. Draw or glue a picture.

I'm ______________________. This is my favorite picture.

This is a picture of ______________.

____

____

____

____

____

____

It's a ______________________ picture.

Edit

K Read and check.

In my writing:

- ☐ I can follow my writing plan.
- ☐ I can use a capital letter for the first letter of each sentence.
- ☐ I can use a period at the end of each sentence.

3 Who lives in this house?

Words to know

badger woods neat messy hard-working
smart shy parties cheerful kind

Read

A **Look at the pictures. What kind of person lives in this house?**

1 ☐ messy **2** ☐ neat **3** ☐ lazy

B **Read.**

Bertie Badger

Bertie Badger lives in the woods.

Bertie is very neat. His home is always clean and it's never messy. Bertie is hard-working and he's smart. There are lots of books in his house.

Bertie is shy. He doesn't like big parties, but he likes talking with one or two friends. He isn't very cheerful, but he is very kind.

Understand

C **Read the sentences and write a ✓ or ✗.**

1 Bertie Badger lives in the woods. ✓
2 Bertie's home is very messy. ☐
3 Bertie has lots of books. ☐
4 Bertie likes big parties. ☐
5 Bertie likes talking with his friends. ☐
6 Bertie is very cheerful. ☐

D **Write the words to complete each pair of opposites.**

silly ~~lazy~~ mean miserable messy

1 hard-working — lazy
2 smart — ________
3 neat — ________
4 kind — ________
5 cheerful — ________

E **Complete the sentences about Bertie Badger with words from D.**

1 Bertie Badger isn't lazy. He's very hard-working.
2 Bertie Badger's house isn't messy. Bertie is very ________.
3 Bertie Badger is a bit miserable. He isn't very ________.
4 Bertie Badger isn't mean. He's very ________.
5 Bertie Badger reads lots of books. He's very ________.

F **Think about Bertie Badger's personality. Which words describe your personality? Does your room show your personality?**

Think

G Think about your favorite characters from books or movies. Where do they live? Write a list.

Character	Home
______________	______________
______________	______________
______________	______________
______________	______________

H **Writing focus**

We use adjectives to describe characters and things in stories.
Bertie is very **neat**.

Look at your answers in **G**. Do you use adjectives?

Plan

I Choose one of the characters from your list in **G**. Complete the chart. Remember to use adjectives.

Character: ______________________________

Personality	Home
______________	______________
______________	______________
______________	______________
______________	______________

Write

J Now write about your favorite character and his/her home. Use your work in **G**, **H** and **I** to help you. Draw or glue a picture.

__________ lives in __________

__________________________________.

__________ is __________

____

____

__________ home is __________________

____

____

Edit

K Read and check.

In my writing:

- [ ] I can follow my writing plan.
- [ ] I can use capital letters and periods correctly in a sentence.
- [ ] I can use adjectives to describe a character and a place.

4 How do animals change?

Words to know

life cycle lay eggs hatch tadpole tail
week grow breathe adult land

Read

A **Look at the pictures. What do you think the text is about?**

B **Read.**

The life cycle of a frog

1 In spring, frogs lay eggs in the water.

2 After a few days, the eggs hatch. The tadpoles are small with long tails.

3 After a few weeks, the tadpoles' legs start to grow.

4 Now the tadpoles have long legs and short tails. They need air to breathe.

5 By summer, the adult frogs can live on land and swim in the water.

Understand

C Match the sentence parts.

1 A frog lays an egg
2 The egg hatches into
3 The tadpole's legs
4 The tadpole needs
5 The frog is

a start to grow.
b an adult.
c air to breathe.
d in the water.
e a tadpole.

D Write the sentences from **C** in the flowchart.

The life cycle of a frog

1 ______________________________

2 ______________________________

3 ______________________________

4 ______________________________

5 ______________________________

E Look at the information in **D**. Number the pictures in the correct order.

F Think about the life cycle of a frog. What other facts do you know about frogs?

Think

G Think about other animals that you know. Make a list of animals that change a lot in their life cycle.

____

____

Plan

H Choose an animal from your list in **G**. Read the questions and write your answers in the flowchart.

1 How does the animal start its life?
2 What does it look like when it is a baby?
3 How does it change?
4 What does it look like when it is an adult?

The life cycle of a ____________

1 ________________________
2 ________________________
3 ________________________
4 ________________________

I **Writing focus**

When we write about steps in a sequence, we write **captions**. A caption is a short piece of text, usually under a picture. Each caption describes one step in the sequence.

Choose the correct caption for this photo.

- ☐ The baby dragonflies don't have wings.
- ☐ The dragonfly lays eggs in the water.
- ☐ The adult dragonfly can fly.

Write

J Now write about the life cycle of your animal. Use your work in **H** and **I** to help you. Draw or glue pictures.

1

2

3

4

Edit

K Read and check.

In my writing:

- [ ] I can follow my writing plan.
- [ ] I can write captions describing pictures.
- [ ] I can write the steps in a sequence in the correct order.
- [ ] I can use capital letters and periods correctly in a sentence.

FOCUS: Parts of a story **OUTPUT:** A fictional story

5 How many days to go?

Words to know

excited   look forward to   vacation   sunhat   bucket
shovel   camera   sunglasses   pack   suitcase

Read

A Look at the text and the pictures. What kind of text is it?

1 ☐ a story   2 ☐ a diary   3 ☐ a postcard

B Read.

Maria's Vacation

Maria is very excited. She's looking forward to her vacation.

When there are three days to go, Maria buys a new sunhat, a bucket, and a shovel.

When there are two days to go, Maria finds her camera and her sunglasses.

When there is one day to go, Maria packs her suitcase.

It's Saturday! Maria goes on vacation! She feels very happy.

Understand

C What does Maria do in the story? Match the sentences parts.

1	Maria buys	a	her camera.
2	Maria packs	b	very happy.
3	Maria feels	c	on vacation.
4	Maria finds	d	her suitcase.
5	Maria goes	e	a sunhat.

D Write the sentences in **C** in the correct order.

1 Maria buys a sunhat.
2 ______
3 ______
4 ______
5 ______

E Complete the sentences with the words in the box.

one day | two days | three days

1 Maria finds her camera two days before her vacation.
2 She packs her suitcase ______ before her vacation.
3 She buys a bucket and shovel ______ before her vacation.
4 She finds her sunglasses ______ before her vacation.
5 She buys a sunhat ______ before her vacation.

F Think about the story. How does Maria feel? How do you feel before you go on vacation?

Think

G Think about things that you look forward to. Make a list.

___

___

___

___

Plan

H Choose one of the things from your list in **G**.
What do you do before it? Complete the timeline.

Three days to go	Two days to go	One day to go	Event
___	___	___	___
___	___	___	___
___	___	___	
___	___	___	

I **Writing focus**

When we write a story, we always write a **title**.

Then we write a **beginning**, a **middle**, and an **ending**.

Beginning: Who are the characters? How do they feel?

Middle: What happens?

End: What happens in the end? How do the characters feel?

Look at Maria's story again. Which parts are the title, the beginning, the middle, and the ending?

Write

J Now write a story about your exciting event. Use your work in **H** and **I** to help you. Draw or glue a picture.

____

____

When there are three days to go, ____________________

____

When there are ____________________

____

When ____________________

____

It's ____________________

Edit

K Read and check.

In my writing:

- ☐ I can follow my writing plan.
- ☐ I can give my story a title.
- ☐ I can write a story with a beginning, a middle, and an ending.
- ☐ I can use capital letters and periods correctly in sentences.

6 Who can you call?

Words to know

emergency police fire department ambulance service
dial operator panic remember accident crime

Read

A Look at the poster. What do you think the number 911 is for?

B Read.

911

The US Emergency Services are the police, fire department, and ambulance service.

- In an emergency, dial 911 from your phone.
- Tell the operator which service you need and what the emergency is.
- Tell the operator where you are.
- Give your name.
- Don't panic. Answer the operator's questions.

Remember! An emergency is a fire, an accident, or a crime.

Understand

C Read the poster in **B** and number the pictures in the correct order.

D Imagine you see a fire. What do you do?
Match the sentences to the flowchart.

1 ______

2 ______

3 ______

4 ______

5 ______

a Give your name.

b Dial 911.

c Answer the operator's questions.

d Ask for the fire department.

e Say where you are.

E Think about the poster in **B**. Where can you see a poster like this? What's the phone number for the emergency services in your country?

Think

F **Think about the different emergency services. Which emergency service can help in these emergencies?**

1 A crime ____________ 2 An accident ____________

Plan

G **Choose an emergency from your list in F. Complete the flowchart. Use the poster in B to help you.**

When there is ____________, dial ____________.

Ask for the ____________.

Tell the operator ____________ and ____________.

Don't ____________.

H **Writing focus**

When we write instructions we use imperative verbs.

Dial 911. Don't panic.

We are careful to write the instructions in the correct order.

Read the sentences and underline the imperative verbs.

1 In the UK, <u>dial</u> 999 when you see a crime.
2 Tell the operator your name.
3 Ask for the police.
4 Don't end the call.

Write

I Now write an emergency services poster for your country. Use your work in **G** and **H** to help you. Draw or glue a picture.

____

In ____________________, the emergency services are

____

In an emergency, dial ____________________.

Ask for ______________________________

____.

Tell the operator ____________________

____

____

____

Edit

J Read and check.

In my writing:

- [ ] I can follow my writing plan.
- [ ] I can use imperative verbs for instructions.
- [ ] I can write instructions in the correct order.

7 Where do you want to live?

Words to know

the country traditional garden cozy peaceful
modern busy city interesting comfortable

Read

A Look at the labels. What do you think the text is about?

B Read.

MY DREAM HOME

My dream home is a traditional house in the country. It has a big garden with lots of flowers. There's a fireplace and a sofa in the living room. It's very cozy and peaceful.

Mateo, 7

My dream home is a modern apartment in a busy city. It has a balcony. There are white walls and there's interesting furniture. It's a very comfortable home.

Camila, 7

Understand

C Read and circle the correct words.

1 Camila's dream home is **traditional** / **modern**.
2 Mateo's dream home is **a house** / **an apartment**.
3 Camila's dream home has **a balcony** / **a garden**.
4 Mateo's dream home has **a fireplace** / **white walls**.
5 Camila's dream home is **peaceful** / **comfortable**.
6 Mateo's dream home is **cozy** / **busy**.

D Look at the texts and the pictures in **B**. Write the words in the correct boxes.

~~the country~~	city	apartment	house
traditional	modern	comfortable	peaceful

Mateo's Dream Home	Camila's Dream Home
the country	

E Think about Camila and Mateo's dream homes. Which home do you like best? Why?

Think

F Think about different types of houses and places you would like to live in. Write a list.

____

____

____

Plan

G Choose your dream home from your list in **F**. Complete the chart.

1 What kind of home is it?	______________
2 Where is it?	______________
3 What can you see outside?	______________
4 What can you see inside?	______________
5 What adjectives describe it?	______________

H **Writing focus**

We can use **labels** to show the important parts of a picture.

Write the correct labels for the picture.

house
garden
pool

Write

I Now write about your dream home. Use your work in **G** and **H** to help you. Draw or glue a picture. Then label it.

My dream home

My dream home is ______________________________ .

It has ______________________________

____

____

____

____

____

____

Edit

J Read and check.

In my writing:

- [ ] I can follow my writing plan.
- [ ] I can use adjectives to describe places.
- [ ] I can label the important parts of a picture.

FOCUS: Main idea and details of a text **OUTPUT:** Informational text

8 What sounds can you make?

Words to know

percussion instrument stomp tap pat
clap click whistle hum voice

Read

A Look at the website. What do you think the text is about?

B Read.

BODY PERCUSSION

You don't need a musical instrument to make music.
You can make music with your body.

You can pat your legs.

You can stomp or tap your feet.

You can clap your hands and you can click your fingers.

You can whistle, hum, or make sounds with your voice.

Put these sounds together and you can make music.
Try it with your friends!

Understand

C **Complete the sentences with the words in the box.**

clicking	clapping	whistling	stomping	patting	tapping

1 He's ____________ his feet.

2 She's ____________ her hands.

3 He's ____________ his fingers.

4 She's ____________ her foot.

5 She's ____________ her legs.

6 He's ____________.

D **Read the text in B and complete the chart.**

whistle	stomp	clap	hum	pat	tap

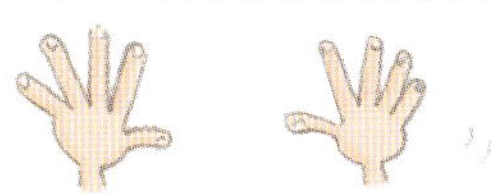		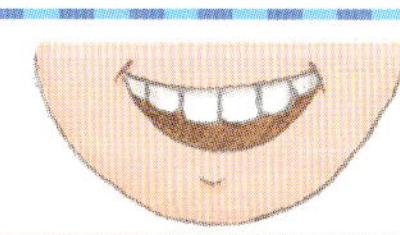
1 ____________	3 ____________	5 ____________
2 ____________	4 ____________	6 ____________

E **Look at the information in D. Complete the sentences.**

1 You can use your hands to ____________ and ____________.

2 You can use your feet to ________________________.

3 You can use your ________________________.

F **Think about the website. Why do people like making music? How does music make you feel?**

Think

G **Think about the different sounds *you* can make. Write a list.**

____

____

Plan

H **Choose some sounds from your list in G. Complete the chart.**

Sound	Body part
____________	____________
____________	____________
____________	____________
____________	____________

I **Writing focus**

When we write an informational text, we write the **main idea**. The main idea tells us what the text is about.

You can make lots of sounds with your body.

Then we write **detail sentences** about the main idea.

You can clap your hands. You can stomp your feet.

Read and write M for the main idea and D for the detail sentences.

1 ____ You can click your fingers.
2 ____ You can make different sounds with your hands.
3 ____ You can clap.

Write

J Now write about the sounds you can make. Use your work in **H** and **I** to help you. Draw or glue a picture.

____

I can ________________

____

____

____

____

____

____

I can make music!

Edit

K Read and check.

In my writing:

- [ ] I can follow my writing plan.
- [ ] I can write the main idea first.
- [ ] I can write detail sentences about the main idea.

FOCUS: The beginning, middle, and ending of a story **OUTPUT:** An imaginative story

9 What do your toys do?

Words to know

robot alive train set fly plane drive
dance puppet floor surprised

Read

A Look at the pictures. What do you think is happening at the beginning of the story?

B Read.

Riki the Robot

It's Monday morning. Riki the robot wants to play, but Ferdi is going to school.

The toys are alone. Riki becomes alive! He rides on the train. He flies in the plane. He drives the cars. He dances with the puppet.

Ferdi comes home. All the toys are on the floor. Ferdi is surprised. "What's going on?" Ferdi asks. But Riki doesn't speak.

Understand

C Who are the characters in the story?

____

____

D Look at the story in **B**. Match the sentence parts.

1 Riki becomes ● — ● a a car.
2 Riki rides ● — ● b a plane.
3 Riki flies ● — ● c with a puppet.
4 Riki drives ● — ● d alive.
5 Riki dances ● — ● e on a train set.

E Think about the story and answer the questions.

bored surprised happy sad worried

1 How do you think Riki feels when he starts to play?

____

2 How do you think Ferdi feels when he comes home?

____

F Think about Riki the robot.
Can toys really become alive?
What are the differences between living and nonliving things?

Think

G **Think about your toys. Write a list.**

____

Plan

H **Choose your favorite toy from your list in G. Complete the notes.**

My favorite toy is a ______________________.

His / Her name is ______________________.

When I'm not at home, I think my toy ______________________

____

I **Writing focus**

Remember, when we write a story, we write a **beginning**, a **middle**, and an **ending**.

In the **beginning**, we can write:

- who the characters are and how they feel
- when the story takes place — It's Monday morning

In the **middle**, we write the events of the story in the correct order.

In the **ending**, we can write:

- what happens in the end — Ferdi comes home …
- how the characters feel — Ferdi is surprised.

Look again at the different parts of the story in B.
Do you like the ending to the story?

Write

J Now write a story about your favorite toy. Use your work in **H** and **I** to help you. Draw or glue a picture.

____

It's ____________________

____

The toys are alone. ____________________

____

____

____

__________ comes home. __________

____

____

Edit

K Read and check.

In my writing:

- ☐ I can follow my writing plan.
- ☐ I can write who my characters are and how they feel.
- ☐ I can write a beginning, a middle, and an ending.

Spelling Master Class

1 Keep a spelling log

A **What words are difficult to spell? Tell the class.**

B **Spelling strategy**

To help us remember difficult words, we can make the difficult letters in each word bigger.

1 Look at the word. Find the difficult letters.

2 Write the word in your spelling log. Make the difficult letters bigger. You can use a different color for the difficult letters.

3 Say the words in your spelling log. You can say the difficult letters louder.

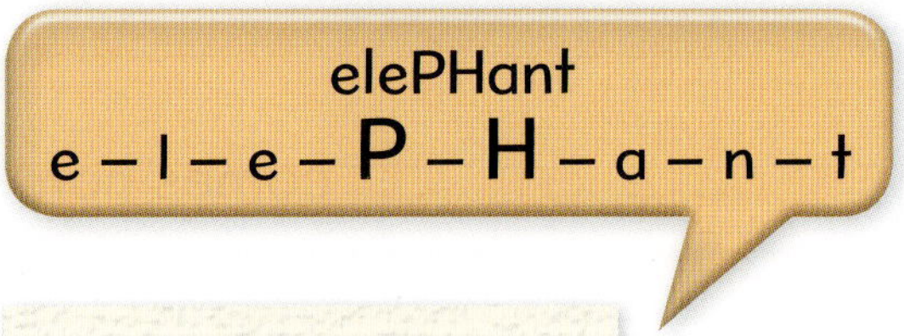

4 Practice writing the words in your spelling log.

C **Find the difficult letters in these words. Write the words and make the difficult letters bigger.**

1 aunt ______

2 climb ______

3 cousin ______

4 tortoise ______

5 friend ______

6 ocean ______

D **Think about your words from A. Write four of your difficult words. Make the difficult letters bigger to help you remember.**

______ ______

______ ______

2 a_e, ay, ai

A **Spelling focus**

We can spell the same sound with different letters.

These words have the same sound:

cake   birthday   paint

B **Say the words. Circle the words with the sound from A.**

cat	name	rain	play	wash	star
lake	glass	crayon	paint	car	say
wait	plate	train	shape	day	tail

C **Write the words from B in the correct circles.**

a + consonant + e

name

a + y

a + i

D **Write more words with the sound from A. Underline *a–e*, *ay*, or *ai*.**

3 Plurals: *-s, -es, -ies*

A **Spelling focus**

When we change a word from singular (one) to plural (more than one), we usually change the spelling.

For most words, we add **s**. rabbit → rabbit**s**

B **Write these words as plurals.**

1 cat ____________ **3** sister ____________

2 tree ____________ **4** school ____________

C **Spelling focus**

When a word ends in *-s*, *-sh*, *-ch*, or *-x*, we add *-es*.

When a word ends in a consonant + *y* , we remove the *-y* and add *-ies*.

D **Look at the words below. Which words need an *-s*, *-es*, or *-ies* to make them plural? Write each word in the chart.**

baby ~~uncle~~ bus family sandwich brother
butterfly brush pen strawberry color box

+s	+es	-y +ies
uncles		

4 e, ea, ee, ey, y

A **Spelling focus**

These words have the same sound.
We can spell it in different ways:

me	pea	baby
see	key	

B **Say the words. Circle the letter or letters that make the sound from A.**

she party sea bee family
key me jeans honey ice cream
monkey green tree be strawberry

C **Write the words from B in the chart.**

e	ea	ee	ey	y
she				

D **Write more words with the sound from A. Underline *e, ea, ee, ey,* or *y*.**

5 i_e, igh, ie, y

A **Spelling focus**

These words have the same sound. We can spell it in different ways:

kite pie night fly

B **Circle the word that does not match.**

1	bike	hide	slide	dry
2	pie	ride	tie	lie
3	cry	sky	like	fly
4	shy	high	light	night
5	why	right	my	shy
6	like	five	night	kite

C **Write the words from B in the correct boxes.**

i + consonant + *e*	*igh*	*ie*	*y*
bike			

D **Write more words with the sound from A. Underline *i_e, igh, ie,* or *y*.**

6 Verb endings: -s, -es

A **Spelling focus**

When we want to write present tense verbs for *He*, *She*, or *It* (the third person form), we usually have to change the verb.

For most third person verbs, we add *-s*.

I walk → He walk**s**

B **Write these verbs in the third person form.**

1	run	______	4	write	______
2	sit	______	5	listen	______
3	play	______	6	jump	______

C **Spelling focus**

When a verb ends in *-s*, *-ch*, *-sh*, *-x*, or *-o* we add *-es* to make the *He*, *She*, or *It* form.

pass	→	pass**es**	fix	→	fix**es**
watch	→	watch**es**	go	→	go**es**
push	→	push**es**			

D **Underline the endings from C in each verb. Then write the verbs in the third person form.**

1	I wa<u>sh</u>	He washes	5	I pass	She ______
2	I go	She ______	6	I touch	It ______
3	I catch	It ______	7	I brush	He ______
4	I mix	He ______	8	I do	She ______

7 ow, o_e, oa

A **Spelling focus**

These words have the same sound. We can spell it in different ways:

phone   snow   coat

B **Say the words. Circle the letters that make the sound from A.**

yellow	boat	goat	grow
home	window	stroke	toad
nose	soap	stone	know

C **Write the words from B in the correct circles.**

o_e

______
______
______
______

ow

yellow
______
______
______

oa

______
______
______
______

D **Write more words with the sound from A. Underline *ow, o_e,* or *oa*.**

______
______

8 Double consonants

A Spelling focus

When we write verbs in the present progressive, we add *-ing*.

I talk → I'm talk**ing**

When a verb ends with a short vowel and one consonant, we double the consonant before adding *-ing*.

I run → I'm run**ning**

B Check (✓) the verbs that need a double consonant before adding *-ing*.

1	☑ run		6	☐ wash		11	☐ sit
2	☐ swim		7	☐ win		12	☐ sing
3	☐ get		8	☐ see		13	☐ tap
4	☐ read		9	☐ clap		14	☐ hum
5	☐ hit		10	☐ jump		15	☐ pat

C Write the verbs in the present progressive.

1. I run — I'm running
2. I tap — I'm ______
3. I skip — I'm ______
4. I hit — I'm ______
5. I pat — I'm ______
6. I swim — I'm ______
7. I hum — I'm ______
8. I clap — I'm ______

9 u_e, ue, ew, ui, oo

A **Spelling focus**

These words have the same sound.
We can spell it in different ways:

tube	new	zoo
glue	fruit	

B **Say the words. Circle the word in each pair that has the sound from A.**

1	run	(ruler)	**8**	moon	mom
2	blue	building	**9**	flute	floor
3	new	now	**10**	glue	goat
4	town	tube	**11**	room	road
5	hoop	hop	**12**	fun	food
6	Sunday	Tuesday	**13**	fruit	foot
7	suitcase	sunhat	**14**	August	June

C **Write the circled words from B in the correct boxes.**

u + consonant + *e*	*oo*	*ew*	*ue*	*ui*
ruler	______	______	______	______
______	______		______	______
______	______		______	
______	______			